CALDECOTT ACTIVITIES

An Avenue for Critical Thinking & Creative Expression

Written by
Kathy O'Steen

Cover Design & Inside Graphics by
Lisbeth Conigliaro

Cover Art by
Steve Volavka

Publishers
T.S. Denison & Co., Inc.
Minneapolis, Minnesota 55431

T.S. DENISON

Standard Book Number: 513-02086-1
Caldecott Activities
Copyright © 1992 by the T.S. Denison & Co., Inc.
Minneapolis, Minnesota 55431

TABLE OF CONTENTS

INTRODUCTION

Caldecott Activities: An Avenue for Critical Thinking & Creative Expression offers ready-to-use student materials to accompany each Caldecott book. The activities consist of vocabulary exercises, high level thinking questions to stimulate critical thinking, and suggested art projects for creative expression.

The vocabulary exercises consist of 5 to 6 vocabulary words, written in context so the student will know how the word is being used in the book. The student proceeds to use the dictionary to obtain the correct meaning of the word. The student writes the correct meaning of the word as well as a sentence using the word to show that he/she fully understands the given vocabulary word.

Questions of a high level of thinking are asked in an exercise to give the student an opportunity to gather meaning from the text. Students must learn to compare, evaluate, analyze, and create.

Art activities that utilize different media such as charcoal, colored chalk, construction paper, tissue paper, poster paint, colored pencils, India ink, watercolors, brayers, styrofoam trays, and water soluble paint are suggested for each book. (*Note: Hairspray may be used in place of a fixative to set chalk drawings.*)

In addition to the various art materials listed for each book, teachers may also want to include a bookholder(s) so that children may study the illustrator's style while they are recreating their favorite scene. Located on page 114 is a pattern for a wooden bookholder. The finished bookholder will tilt backwards to hold the book which protects it from spills. A plastic recipe bookholder may also be used.

Additional activities for science, social studies, math, and language arts are suggested with several different books.

When a student finishes a book, he/she is conferenced by an adult, such as a parent volunteer, student teacher, cross-age tutor, or teacher. The child is asked questions about the story and the vocabulary. The student's work is evaluated for correctness of sentence structure, complete sentences, and spelling. A final grade is given by the teacher on the conference form provided for each child. The conference form is kept in a separate folder for each child along with the child's work.

The finished art picture and worksheets may be stapled onto a 12" x 18" piece of black construction paper which is filed alphabetically by the student's last name into a box. At the end of the year a student's work is collated and put into a spiral-bound book labeled "My Caldecott Portfolio." The work may be displayed and sent home after Open House.

ABRAHAM LINCOLN

Caldecott Medal: 1940   **Illustrators: Ingri & Edgar D'Aulaire**

VOCABULARY: Look up the bold-faced word in the dictionary. Write a definition. Use the word in a sentence of your own.

1. . . . there stood a cabin of roughly **hewn** logs.

   Definition: _____

   Sentence: _____

   _____

2. . . . flames flickered gaily on the **hearth**.

   Definition: _____

   Sentence: _____

   _____

3. . . . little **linsey** shirts ready for him.

   Definition: _____

   Sentence: _____

   _____

4. Slowly the wilderness changed into a **homestead**.

   Definition: _____

   Sentence: _____

   _____

5. . . . the strong boys were **strutting** about like cocks . . .

   Definition: _____

   Sentence: _____

   _____

ABRAHAM LINCOLN

QUESTIONS:

1. Is this book real or fantasy? _____
   Why? _____
   _____

2. What does the word **biography** mean? _____
   _____

3. Why did Abe's father move from Kentucky to Indiana? (Copy the answer from the book exactly.)
   _____
   _____
   _____

4. What kind of life do you think Abe had? _____
   _____

5. What does the phrase, "Even quicker than his legs ran his wit" mean?_____
   _____
   _____
   _____

6. Tell about Abe's first experience with slavery. _____
   _____
   _____

7. How did Lincoln get the nickname of Honest Abe? _____
   _____
   _____

8. What is the name of Lincoln's most famous speech?_____
   _____

ART PROJECT:
   Choose your favorite picture from the book to copy.

   Materials Needed: white construction paper
   drawing pencils
   colored chalk
   fixative
   bookholder

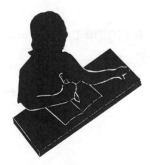

ALWAYS ROOM FOR ONE MORE

Caldecott Medal: 1966   **Illustrator: Nonny Hogrogian**

VOCABULARY: Look up the bold-faced word in the dictionary. Write a definition. Use the word in a sentence of your own.

1. There was a wee house in the **heather**.

    Definition: _____

    Sentence: _____

    _____

2. And his **bairns** to the number of ten.

    Definition: _____

    Sentence: _____

    _____

3. There's room **galore**.

    Definition: _____

    Sentence: _____

    _____

4. A **tinker** came first . . .

    Definition: _____

    Sentence: _____

    _____

5. And they **gawked** at the place where the house stood before.

    Definition: _____

    Sentence: _____

    _____

6. He **hailed** them all in as he stood at the door.

    Definition: _____

    Sentence: _____

    _____

ALWAYS ROOM FOR ONE MORE

QUESTIONS:

1. How many children did Lachie MacLachlan have? _____

2. What was the author's word for "children"? _____
   _____

3. How many people did MacLachlan invite into his house? _____

4. Do you think Lachie MacLachlan was a good man? _____

   Why? _____
   _____

5. What happened to MacLachlan's house?_____
   _____

6. How did MacLachlan's guests say thank-you?_____
   _____

7. How did the story make you feel? _____
   _____

   Why? _____
   _____

ART PROJECT:
Choose your favorite picture from the book to copy.

Materials Needed: white construction paper
                   thin black felt marker
                   colored chalk (use lightly)
                   tissue (use to rub the chalk after it is on the paper)
                   fixative
                   bookholder

Name _____

ANIMALS OF THE BIBLE

Caldecott Medal: 1938   **Illustrator: Dorothy P. Lathrop**

VOCABULARY: Look up the bold-faced word in the dictionary. Write a definition. Use the word in a sentence of your own.

1. . . . let them have **dominion** over the fish of the sea.

   Definition: _____

   Sentence: _____

2. The serpent **beguiled** me and I did eat.

   Definition: _____

   Sentence: _____

3. . . . shalt **pitch** it within . . .

   Definition: _____

   Sentence: _____

4. . . . to see if the waters were **abated** from off the face of the ground.

   Definition: _____

   Sentence: _____

5. . . . emptied her pitcher into the **trough**.

   Definition: _____

   Sentence: _____

6. . . . to make an **atonement** for him.

   Definition: _____

   Sentence: _____

7. . . . the angel of the Lord stood in the way of an **adversary**.

   Definition: _____

   Sentence: _____

8. . . . she **thrust** herself unto the wall.

   Definition: _____

   Sentence: _____

9. . . . he swalloweth the ground with fierceness and **rage**.

   Definition: _____

   Sentence: _____

ANIMALS OF THE BIBLE

1. How did the serpent tempt the woman? _____
   _____
   _____

2. What did God command Noah to do? _____
   _____

3. How was the dove used by Noah? _____
   _____

4. How was Abraham's son saved from being slain? _____
   _____
   _____

5. What gave David the confidence to fight with the Philistines? _____
   _____

6. What is **Leviathan** a symbol of? _____

7. Describe 3 things God does to take care of the animals.
   1) _____
   2) _____
   3) _____

8. How did Daniel's faith in God help him in the den of lions? _____
   _____
   _____

ART PROJECT:
Choose your favorite picture from the book to copy.

Materials Needed: white construction paper
charcoal
India ink
bookholder

Name _____

ARROW TO THE SUN

Caldecott Medal: 1975   **Illustrator: Gerald McDermott**

VOCABULARY: Look up the bold-faced word in the dictionary. Write a definition. Use the word in a sentence of your own.

1. . . . and it came to the **pueblo**.

   Definition: _____

   Sentence: _____

   _____

2. They **mocked** him and chased him away.

   Definition: _____

   Sentence: _____

   _____

3. . . . but continued to **tend** his crops.

   Definition: _____

   Sentence: _____

   _____

4. Then the boy went to Arrow Maker, who was a **wise** man.

   Definition: _____

   Sentence: _____

   _____

5. You must pass through the four **chambers** of ceremony.

   Definition: _____

   Sentence: _____

   _____

6. I will **endure** these trials.

   Definition: _____

   Sentence: _____

   _____

7. When the boy came from the Kiva of Lightning, he was **transformed**.

   Definition: _____

   Sentence: _____

   _____

ARROW TO THE SUN

QUESTIONS:

1. Who was the boy's father? _____

   _____

2. Explain who the boy visited to find his father._____

   _____

3. How did the boy reach his father? _____

   _____

4. List the trials the boy endured: _____

   _____

   _____

   _____

   _____

   _____

5. How did the people celebrate the boy's return? _____

   _____

6. How was the boy filled with the power of the sun? _____

   _____

7. What symbol does Mr. McDermott use for the sun throughout the book? Draw it here:

ART PROJECT:
Choose your favorite picture from the book to copy. Be aware of the symmetry in this book.

Materials Needed: black construction paper
colored chalk
fixative
bookholder

READING AND WRITING ACTIVITY:
Use an encyclopedia and read about the Pueblo Indians. Write a short report about them.

Materials Needed: writing paper
encyclopedia

Name _____

ASHANTI TO ZULU
AFRICAN TRADITIONS

Caldecott Medal: 1977   **Illustrators: Leo & Diane Dillon**

Before you read this book, you should know that the Dillons have tried to include a man, a woman, a child, their living quarters, an artifact, and a local animal in each picture. Also, check the last page of this book. It is a map. You might enjoy locating each tribe as you read about the tribe.

VOCABULARY: This book is full of many new and different words that come from Africa. Enjoy trying to pronounce them:

Chagga   Dagon   Hausa   Ndaka   Masai   Ewe   Fanti   Rendille

Look up the word **artifact**.

Definition: _____

Sentence: _____

QUESTIONS:

1. What are 3 artifacts you found in three pictures?

    1) _____

    2) _____

    3) _____

2. After reading about these different tribes, is there any one tribe you would like to live with?

    _____

    _____

    Why or why not? _____

    _____

ART PROJECT:

First, compare *Ashanti to Zulu* and *Why Mosquitoes Buzz in People's Ears*. Both of these books are done by the Dillons. Note the very different techniques they used. Choose your favorite picture from the book to copy.

Materials Needed: white construction paper   fixative
                     colored chalk or watercolors   bookholder

BABOUSHKA AND THE THREE KINGS

Caldecott Medal: 1961   **Illustrator: Nicolas Sidjakov**

VOCABULARY: Look up the bold-faced word in the dictionary. Write a definition. Use the word in a sentence of your own.

1. The old woman took pride in the clean comfort of her **meager** home.

   Definition: _____

   Sentence: _____

   _____

2. Leading the **procession** was a magnificent sleigh.

   Definition: _____

   Sentence: _____

   _____

3. . . . wearing jeweled crowns and **cloaks** of crimson and ermine.

   Definition: _____

   Sentence: _____

   _____

4. . . . and behind them **trudged** men on foot.

   Definition: _____

   Sentence: _____

   _____

5. . . . and to **rejoice** in his birth.

   Definition: _____

   Sentence: _____

   _____

6. There is no time to **linger**.

   Definition: _____

   Sentence: _____

   _____

BABOUSHKA AND THE THREE KINGS

QUESTIONS:

1. In what country does this story take place? _____
   _____

2. What legend in America is similar to Baboushka? _____
   _____

3. What kind of person was Baboushka? _____
   _____

4. Who came to visit Baboushka? _____

5. What did Baboushka search for? _____
   _____

6. What did Baboushka mean when she said, "Morning is wiser than evening."? _____
   _____
   _____

7. How can a gift be both poor and precious? _____
   _____

   Give an example: _____
   _____

ART PROJECT:
   Choose your favorite picture from the book to copy.

   Materials Needed: white construction paper
           watercolors
           thin black felt pen
           colored chalk
           fixative
           bookholder

Name _____

THE BIG SNOW

Caldecott Medal: 1949   **Illustrators & Authors: Berta & Elmer Hader**

VOCABULARY: Look up the bold-faced word in the dictionary. Write a definition. Use the word in a sentence of your own.

1. Mrs. Chipmunk, with her cheek **pouches** full of seeds.

   Definition: _____

   Sentence: _____

   _____

2. "No, indeed," replied the **cardinals**.

   Definition: _____

   Sentence: _____

   _____

3. Every day during the **harvest** season. . .

   Definition: _____

   Sentence: _____

   _____

4. . . . the mice and the rabbits came out to dance and **frolic**.

   Definition: _____

   Sentence: _____

   _____

5. A blanket of snow covered the **meadows**. . .

   Definition: _____

   Sentence: _____

   _____

6. . . . the hills, the **valleys** . . .

   Definition: _____

   Sentence: _____

   _____

THE BIG SNOW

QUESTIONS:

1. Why didn't some birds fly south? _____

   _____

2. Make a list of the birds that migrate south and those that stay through the winter.

   MIGRATE   STAY

   _____   _____

   _____   _____

   _____   _____

3. Why do you think the people fed the animals rather than let them fend for themselves?

   _____

   _____

4. List the animals that hibernate.

   _____   _____

   _____   _____

   _____   _____

5. What does it mean when the ground hog sees his shadow? _____

   _____

5. What do the animals do to prepare for winter if they do not migrate or hibernate?

   _____

   _____

   _____

ART PROJECT:
   Choose your favorite picture from the book to copy.

   Materials Needed: white construction paper
                      charcoal sticks
                      colored chalk
                      fixative
                      bookholder

Name _____

THE BIGGEST BEAR

Caldecot Medal: 1953   **Illustrator: Lynd Ward**

VOCABULARY: Look up the bold-faced word in the dictionary. Write a definition. Use the word in a sentence of your own.

1. Johnny Orchard lived on the farm **farthest** up the valley . . .

    Definition: _____

    Sentence: _____

    _____

2. . . . and they were known as Orchard's **orchard**.

    Definition: _____

    Sentence: _____

    _____

3. . . . he always felt **humiliated**.

    Definition: _____

    Sentence: _____

    _____

4. He liked the **mash** for the chickens.

    Definition: _____

    Sentence: _____

    _____

5. He was a **trial** . . .

    Definition: _____

    Sentence: _____

    _____

6. . . . and a **tribulation** to the whole valley.

    Definition: _____

    Sentence: _____

    _____

THE BIGGEST BEAR

QUESTIONS:

1. Why did the neighbors think the bear was a trial and a tribulation? _____
   _____
   _____

2. How do you feel about the bear going into other people's food supplies? _____
   _____
   _____

3. Why do you think Johnny was willing to take the bear into the forest the third time and take a gun? _____
   _____
   _____

4. What do you think about the ending? _____
   _____

5. How would you have changed the ending? _____
   _____
   _____

6. When Johnny brought the bear cub home, did he realize how big it would become?
   _____
   Why was that a problem? _____
   _____

7. Can wild creatures be tamed? _____
   Why? _____
   _____

ART PROJECT:
   Choose your favorite picture from the book to copy.
   Copy the words very carefully at the bottom of your picture from the page that tells about the picture.

   Materials Needed: tan or white construction paper
                     charcoal
                     black felt pen
                     fixative
                     bookholder

BLACK AND WHITE

Caldecott Medal: 1991   **Illustrator: David Macaulay**

VOCABULARY: Look up the bold-faced word in the dictionary. Write a definition. Use the word in a sentence of your own.

1. The **journey** will take all night.

   Definition: _____

   Sentence: _____

   _____

2. . . . approach the **boulders**.

   Definition: _____

   Sentence: _____

   _____

3. Amusement quickly turned to **amazement**.

   Definition: _____

   Sentence: _____

   _____

4. The driver **clambers** back into the cab. . .

   Definition: _____

   Sentence: _____

   _____

5. . . . train is still temporarily **delayed**.

   Definition: _____

   Sentence: _____

   _____

6. So Rail **regrets** any inconvenience.

   Definition: _____

   Sentence: _____

   _____

BLACK AND WHITE

QUESTIONS:

1. What does the author mean by "udder chaos?" _____

   _____

   _____

2. Why does the boy's journey take all night? _____

   _____

   _____

3. Notice Macaulay's use of camouflage. What is camouflaged throughout the story from beginning

   to end? _____

   _____

   _____

4. Notice the passengers awaiting the arrival of the eight-thirteen. Name 3 things they do to

   pass the time away.

   1) _____

   2) _____

   3) _____

5. Why did amusement turn to amazement when the boy saw the driver jump down from the train

   and shout at the boulders? _____

   _____

   _____

6. How does the prisoner make his escape? Where does he end his journey? _____

   _____

   _____

7. What is the meaning of "No matter how far Holstein cows go, they always come back when they

   want to be milked"? _____

   _____

   _____

ART PROJECT:
   Choose your favorite picture from the book to copy.

   Materials Needed: construction paper   charcoal pencils
                  newspaper   watercolors
                  black felt pen   oil pastels
                  bookholder

CHANTICLEER AND THE FOX

Caldecott Medal: 1959   **Illustrator: Barbara Cooney**

VOCABULARY: Look up the bold-faced word in the dictionary. Write a definition. Use the word in a sentence of your own.

1. Once upon a time a poor **widow**. . .

    Definition: _____

    Sentence: _____

    _____

2. By careful **management** she was able to care for herself. . .

    Definition: _____

    Sentence: _____

    _____

3. She had only 3 large **sows**.

    Definition: _____

    Sentence: _____

    _____

4. . . . his legs and toes were like **azure**.

    Definition: _____

    Sentence: _____

    _____

5. His comb was. . . **turreted** like a castle wall . . .

    Definition: _____

    Sentence: _____

    _____

6. . . . the rooster **nimbly** broke away from his mouth . . .

    Definition: _____

    Sentence: _____

    _____

CHANTICLEER AND THE FOX

QUESTIONS:

1. What is the setting for the story? _____
   _____

2. Describe Chanticleer's bad dream. _____
   _____
   _____

3. Who tricked whom in this story? _____

   Explain. _____
   _____
   _____

4. Was there more than one trick? _____

   Explain. _____
   _____
   _____

5. How did Chanticleer escape? _____
   _____

6. What does it mean to be "vain"? _____
   _____

   Who was vain in the story? _____

ART PROJECT:
Choose your favorite picture from the book to copy.

Materials Needed: white construction paper
black India ink
brush
pin (to scrape away picture)
bookholder

Directions: Using a brush, cover your paper with ink.
Let dry. Scratch out picture with a pin.

CINDERELLA

Caldecott Medal: 1955   **Illustrator: Marcia Brown**

VOCABULARY: Look up the bold-faced word in the dictionary. Write a definition. Use the word in a sentence of your own.

1. . . . took for his second wife the proudest and **haughtiest** woman. . .

   Definition: _____

   Sentence: _____

   _____

2. She had two daughters. . . bad **disposition** and all.

   Definition: _____

   Sentence: _____

   _____

3. Cinderella slept on a wretched straw pallet in the miserable **garret**.

   Definition: _____

   Sentence: _____

   _____

4. . . . the pumpkin turned into a beautiful coach, **gilded** with pure gold.

   Definition: _____

   Sentence: _____

   _____

5. Thus **arrayed**, Cinderella climbed into the coach.

   Definition: _____

   Sentence: _____

   _____

6. The sisters were completely **astonished**.

   Definition: _____

   Sentence: _____

   _____

CINDERELLA

QUESTIONS:

1. Name the things the fairy godmother had to change to prepare Cinderella for the ball.

    _____

    _____

    _____

    _____

2. How did Cinderella treat her sisters at the end of the story? _____

    _____

    What did she do for them? _____

    _____

    Tell what you would have done if you were Cinderella. _____

    _____

    _____

3. Write a different ending for the story. _____

    _____

    _____

    _____

    _____

    _____

    _____

ART PROJECT:

Choose your favorite picture from the book to copy.

Materials Needed: white construction paper
colored chalk
thin black marker
fixative
bookholder

Name _____

DRUMMER HOFF

Caldecott Medal: 1968   **Illustrator: Ed Emberly**

VOCABULARY: Look up the bold-faced word in the dictionary. Write a definition. Use the word in a sentence of your own.

1. Private Parriage brought the **carriage**.

   Definition: _____

   Sentence: _____

   _____

2. Corporal Farrel brought the **barrel**.

   Definition: _____

   Sentence: _____

   _____

3. Sergeant Chowder brought the **powder**.

   Definition: _____

   Sentence: _____

   _____

4. Captain Bammer brought the **rammer**.

   Definition: _____

   Sentence: _____

   _____

QUESTIONS:

1. What is the main idea of the story? _____

   _____

2. What is the job of the main character? _____

   _____

3. List 4 of the rhymes in this story.

   1) _____

   2) _____

   3) _____

   4) _____

4. Who gave the order? _____

    What was the order? _____

5. Who brought the first piece?_____

    What was it? _____

6. What is "shot"? _____

    Who brought it? _____

7. List the characters in order of their army rank from lowest to highest. _____

    _____

    _____

    _____

8. Why do you think the last page shows the cannon being used by birds and insects, as well as being covered with flowers? _____

    _____

ART PROJECT:

Choose your favorite picture from the book to copy.

Materials Needed: white construction paper
styrofoam meat tray
scissors
blunt pencil
brayer
tube ink
felt marker
bookholder

Directions: Trim off the curved edge from the meat tray.
Draw your picture on the meat tray with a pencil.
Press hard to make a groove.
Roll colored ink onto your print.
Press your picture face down on the drawing paper.
Allow your picture to dry for one day.
Fill it in with the colored markers.

DUFFY AND THE DEVIL

Caldecott Medal: 1974   **Illustrator: Margot Zemach**

VOCABULARY: Look up the bold-faced word in the dictionary. Write a definition. Use the word in a sentence of your own.

1. **Squire** Lovel of Trove . . .

   Definition: _____

   Sentence: _____

   _____

2. **Blubbering**, bawling girl. . .

   Definition: _____

   Sentence: _____

   _____

3. She **gallivants** with the boys all day long. . .

   Definition: _____

   Sentence: _____

   _____

4. Good **riddance** to bad rummage. . .

   Definition: _____

   Sentence: _____

   _____

5. . . . **frolicking** away the time while the corn was grinding.

   Definition: _____

   Sentence: _____

   _____

6. Lazy **bufflehead**. . .

   Definition: _____

   Sentence: _____

   _____

DUFFY AND THE DEVIL

QUESTIONS:

1. What folktale does *Duffy And The Devil* remind you of? _____
   _____

2. It is a story similar to one you know with a few changes. Which one do you think is funnier?
   _____

   Why? _____
   _____

3. Who did the spinning for Duffy? _____
   _____

4. How did Duffy learn his name? _____
   _____

5. Did you think it was fair when the knitted articles the squire was wearing, as well as everything
   in the house, disappeared? _____

   Why? _____
   _____

6. Why was there a horseshoe on the squire's door?_____
   _____

7. Why was Old Jones with the witches? _____
   _____

8. Why didn't Duffy ever knit again? _____
   _____

ART PROJECT:
Choose your favorite picture from the book to copy.

Materials Needed: white construction paper
watercolors
thin black felt tip pen
bookholder

Name _____

THE EGG TREE

Caldecott Medal: 1951   **Illustrator & Author: Katherine Milhous**

VOCABULARY: Look up the bold-faced word in the dictionary. Write a definition. Use the word in a sentence of your own.

1. . . . and even in the butter **churn**.

    Definition: _____

    Sentence: _____

    _____

2. Just then she saw the **attic** stairs.

    Definition: _____

    Sentence: _____

    _____

3. Katy began to climb the **creaking** stairs.

    Definition: _____

    Sentence: _____

    _____

QUESTIONS:

1. What is the main idea of the story? _____

    _____

2. What does Grandma say the Egg Tree brings? _____

3. Describe the Egg Tree. _____

    _____

    _____

4. What presents did children bring for the tree? _____

    _____

ART PROJECT:

The pictures in the book are copies of flat, simple designs in the Pennsylvania Dutch tradition. The color scheme includes: pink, gray, bright yellow, red, and blue.
Choose a design from the book to copy.

Materials Needed: white construction paper   felt pen
                          watercolors   bookholder

FABLES

Caldecott Medal: 1981   **Illustrator: Arnold Lobel**

VOCABULARY: Look up the bold-faced word in the dictionary. Write a definition. Use the word in a sentence of your own.

1. They are messy and **entwined**.

   Definition: _____

   Sentence: _____

   _____

2. The crocodile rushed back to his bedroom in a state of great **distress**.

   Definition: _____

   Sentence: _____

   _____

3. I am **accustomed** to it.

   Definition: _____

   Sentence: _____

   _____

4. "It is foolhardy to **venture** out on a day like this."

   Definition: _____

   Sentence: _____

   _____

5. It is a sad **predicament**.

   Definition: _____

   Sentence: _____

   _____

6. He licked his whiskers in **anticipation**.

   Definition: _____

   Sentence: _____

   _____

FABLES

1. What is a fable? _____
   _____

2. Are these fables fact or fantasy? _____

   Why? _____

3. Which fable is your favorite? _____
   _____

   Why do you like it best? _____
   _____

4. Compare the character in your favorite fable with yourself.
   Tell one way in which you are alike, and one way in which you are different.

   Alike: _____
   _____

   Different: _____
   _____

5. What is the lesson your favorite character learned? _____
   _____
   _____

ART PROJECT:
   Choose your favorite picture from the book to copy.

   Materials Needed: white construction paper
   watercolors
   black felt pen
   colored chalk
   fixative
   bookholder

Name _____

FINDERS KEEPERS

Caldecott Medal: 1952   **Illustrator: Nicolas Mordvinoff**

VOCABULARY: Look up the bold-faced word in the dictionary. Write a definition. Use the word in a sentence of your own.

1. His cart **bogged** in a soft spot on the road.
   Definition: _____
   Sentence: _____
   _____

2. The first person they met was an **apprentice** barber.
   Definition: _____
   Sentence: _____
   _____

3. Just then a big dog came **ambling** down the road.
   Definition: _____
   Sentence: _____
   _____

QUESTIONS:

1. What did Nap and Winkle argue over? _____
2. Who did they ask to help solve their problem?_____
   _____

3. How did the big dog solve their problem? _____
   _____

4. What lesson did Nap and Wrinkle learn? _____
   _____

ART PROJECT:

The artist used large flat areas of color such as red and pale yellow with black lines and shapes.
Choose your favorite picture to make a collage.
Cut the figures out of construction paper and glue them onto a piece of drawing paper.
Outline and add detail with pen and ink.

Materials Needed: white, red, and yellow construction paper
glue
black felt pen
bookholder

THE FOOL OF THE WORLD AND THE FLYING SHIP

Caldecott Medal: 1969   **Illustrator: Uri Shulevitz**

VOCABULARY: Look up the bold-faced word in the dictionary. Write a definition. Use the word in a sentence of your own.

1. **. . . parcels** of food . . .

Definition: _____

Sentence: _____

_____

2. So he **trudged** merrily along . . .

Definition: _____

Sentence: _____

_____

3. . . . when he met an **ancient** old man . . .

Definition: _____

Sentence: _____

_____

4. . . . a thousand **versts**.

Definition: _____

Sentence: _____

_____

5. . . . with a **fagot** of wood . . .

Definition: _____

Sentence: _____

_____

6. If you are such a **cunning** fellow . . .

Definition: _____

Sentence: _____

_____

THE FOOL OF THE WORLD AND THE FLYING SHIP

QUESTIONS:

1. How did the fool's parents feel about him?_____

   _____

2. Describe how the fool got the ship. _____

   _____

   _____

3. List the people the fool took into the ship and what they could do to help the fool. Tell if each

   helped the fool. _____

   _____

   _____

   _____

   _____

4. What are your feelings about the King? _____

   _____

5. Was the fool a fool?_____Why?_____

   _____

   _____

ART PROJECT:
   Choose your favorite picture from the book to copy.

   Materials Needed: white construction paper
   water colors
   black felt pen
   colored chalk
   fixative
   bookholder

ACTIVITY:
   Make up a play or puppet show about *The Fool of the World.*
   Have partners work with you on this.
   Present your play/puppet show to the class when you are finished.

FROG WENT A-COURTIN'

Caldecott Medal: 1956   **Illustrator: Feodor Rojankovsky**

VOCABULARY: Look up the bold-faced word in the dictionary. Write a definition. Use the word in a sentence of your own.

1. Where he most **tenderly** did call:

   Definition: _____

   Sentence: _____

   _____

2. "Oh, Mistress Mouse, are you **within**?"

   Definition: _____

   Sentence: _____

   _____

3. "Way down **yonder** in a hollow tree."

   Definition: _____

   Sentence: _____

   _____

4. Then Uncle Rat gave his **consent**.

   Definition: _____

   Sentence: _____

   _____

5. Next to come in was a **nimble** flea.

   Definition: _____

   Sentence: _____

   _____

6. Frog's **bridle** and saddle . . .

   Definition: _____

   Sentence: _____

   _____

FROG WENT A-COURTIN'

QUESTIONS:

1. Explain why this story is fact or fantasy. _____
   _____

2. Do you think the story would make a good song? _____
   Why? _____

3. Which characters were married? _____
   _____

4. What did the couple have to get before they were married? _____
   _____

5. Name the food that was served at the wedding breakfast. _____
   _____
   _____

6. How did the celebration end? _____
   _____

7. In what country do you think this story takes place? _____
   _____

8. Write a different ending for this story. _____
   _____
   _____
   _____
   _____

9. What kind of pattern do you see in the pictures of this book? _____
   _____
   _____

ART PROJECT:
Choose your favorite picture from the book to copy.
Using a thin marker, copy the words for your picture from the page you copied.

Materials Needed: white construction paper
colored chalk
tissue (use to rub the picture to shade)
fixative
bookholder

THE FUNNY LITTLE WOMAN

Caldecott Medal: 1973   **Illustrator: Blair Lent**

VOCABULARY: Look up the bold-faced word in the dictionary. Write a definition. Use the word in a sentence of your own.

1. "I smell the smell of **humankind.**"

   Definition: _____

   Sentence: _____

   _____

2. . . . who like to make **dumplings** out of rice.

   Definition: _____

   Sentence: _____

   _____

3. . . . "**ungrateful** dumpling."

   Definition: _____

   Sentence: _____

   _____

4. . . . **scolded** the little woman.

   Definition: _____

   Sentence: _____

   _____

5. "I have," said a very **stern** Jizo.

   Definition: _____

   Sentence: _____

   _____

QUESTIONS:

1. In what country does this story take place? _____

2. Is the story fact or fantasy? _____

   Why? _____

   _____

3. Look carefully at the picture of the old woman above ground and below ground. What does the artist do to make the pictures below ground seem scary or uninviting?

   _____

   _____

4. Do you think the old woman had a right to take the magic paddle? _____
   Why? _____

   _____

5. Do you think the old woman should have become rich? _____
   Why? _____

   _____

6. What did you find funny in the story? _____

   _____

   _____

7. Write a different ending for the story. _____

   _____

   _____

   _____

   _____

   _____

   _____

   _____

ART PROJECT:

Choose your favorite underground picture from the book to copy.

Materials Needed: gray or light brown construction paper   white glue
thin black pen (for outlining)   green and black marker pens
colored chalk   bookholder

Directions: Draw with ink. Outline with felt pen. Color with chalk.
After picture is complete, use white glue to make the roots coming down. Let dry for a day and then color over glue with green and black marker pens. This will give you a collage effect.

THE GIRL WHO LOVED WILD HORSES

Caldecott Medal: 1979   **Illustrator & Writer: Paul Goble**

VOCABULARY: Look up the bold-faced word in the dictionary. Write a definition. Use the word in a sentence of your own.

1. . . . to find them shelter from the winter **blizzards**.

    Definition: _____

    Sentence: _____

    _____

2. She stayed with them in the **meadows**. . .

    Definition: _____

    Sentence: _____

    _____

3. Horses were rearing up on their hind legs and **snorting** in terror.

    Definition: _____

    Sentence: _____

    _____

4. In an instant the **herd** was galloping away. . .

    Definition: _____

    Sentence: _____

    _____

5. . . . **pursued** by the thunder and lightning.

    Definition: _____

    Sentence: _____

    _____

6. The people searched everywhere for the girl and the **vanished** horses.

    Definition: _____

    Sentence: _____

    _____

THE GIRL WHO LOVED WILD HORSES

QUESTIONS:

1. What is a legend? _____

_____

2. What kind of legend do you think this story could be? _____

_____

3. What happened to the horses when the storm struck? _____

_____

4. What did the stallion ask the girl? _____

_____

5. How did the girl feel when she was home? _____

_____

6. What did the girl bring her parents every year? _____

_____

7. What happened when the girl died? _____

_____

ART PROJECT:
Choose the picture you like the best from the book to copy.

Materials Needed: white construction paper
    black felt pen
    colored chalk or colored pencils
    fixative
    bookholder

Name _____

THE GLORIOUS FLIGHT

Caldecott Medal: 1984   **Illustrators: Alice & Martin Provensen**

VOCABULARY: Look up the bold-faced word in the dictionary. Write a definition. Use the word in a sentence of your own.

1. . . . **soars** a great airship.

   Definition: _____

   Sentence: _____

   _____

2. They toast the valiant **aeronaut**. . .

   Definition: _____

   Sentence: _____

   _____

3. They toast the **valiant** aeronaut. . .

   Definition: _____

   Sentence: _____

   _____

4. He sits **motionless**.

   Definition: _____

   Sentence: _____

   _____

5. The French coast **disappears**.

   Definition: _____

   Sentence: _____

   _____

6. The motor coughs, **sputters**.

   Definition: _____

   Sentence: _____

   _____

THE GLORIOUS FLIGHT

QUESTIONS:

1. Do you think this story is real or imaginary? _____
   Why? _____
2. In what year does this story begin? _____
   What year does Bleriot cross the English Channel? _____
   How many years difference? _____
3. Write ONE single word to describe Papa Bleriot. _____
4. How long was papa's flight? _____
5. Which of papa's planes made the flight? _____
   _____
6. Why does papa sit motionless and let the plane go where it will? _____
   _____
7. Was papa flying high or low over the Channel? _____
   What was said in the story that helped you answer this question? _____
   _____

ART PROJECT:
Choose your favorite picture from the book to copy.

Materials Needed: white construction paper
watercolor
white tempera paint
tissue paper
chalk
fixative
bookholder

SCIENCE PROJECT:
Go to the library. Get a book on how to design paper airplanes. Design some airplanes. Keep a record of which plane flies the highest, the farthest.

Record — Height: _____   Distance: _____

RESEARCH:
Look in an encyclopedia. Find out how wide the English Channel is from Calais to Dover.

Width: _____

Name _____

HEY, AL

Caldecott Medal: 1987   **Illustrator: Richard Egielski**

VOCABULARY: Look up the bold-faced word in the dictionary. Write a definition. Use the word in a sentence of your own.

1. Al and Eddie were **ferried** thousands of feet.

    Definition: _____

    Sentence: _____

    _____

2. Waterfalls **cascaded** into shimmering pools.

    Definition: _____

    Sentence: _____

    _____

3. The days passed **blissfully**.

    Definition: _____

    Sentence: _____

    _____

4. . . . this was **ecstasy**.

    Definition: _____

    Sentence: _____

    _____

5. Tail feathers **plumed**.

    Definition: _____

    Sentence: _____

    _____

6. But Eddie, in a **frenzy** . . .

    Definition: _____

    Sentence: _____

    _____

HEY, AL

QUESTIONS:

1. Explain two reasons why Eddie and Al were so miserable.

   1)_____

   2)_____

2. What event changed Al and Eddie's lives?_____

   _____

   _____

3. Where were Al and Eddie transported? _____

   _____

4. If you were Al, would you have made the same decision he did? _____

   Explain:_____

   _____

5. What did the author mean when he said, "But ripe fruit soon spoils"? _____

   _____

   _____

6. How did Al and Eddie make their escape from the island? _____

   _____

7. Explain the term "Paradise lost is sometimes Heaven found." _____

   _____

   _____

   _____

8. Notice the illustrator's pictures. What is unique about each picture? _____

   _____

   _____

ART PROJECT:
Copy your favorite picture from the book.

Materials Needed: construction paper   black felt pen
watercolors   colored markers
colored chalk   bookholder

If you enjoyed this book about Al and Eddie, the author, Arthur Yorinks, and illustrator, Richard Egielski, have written *Sid and Sol, Louis the Fish*, and *It Happened in Pinsk*.

JUMANJI

Caldecott Medal: 1982   **Illustrator: Chris Van Allsburg**

VOCABULARY: Look up the bold-faced word in the dictionary. Write a definition. Use the word in a sentence of your own.

1. But their laughter slowly turned to silence until Peter **slouched** into the chair.

    Definition: _____

    Sentence: _____

    _____

2. She had a look of **absolute** horror.

    Definition: _____

    Sentence: _____

    _____

3. Bitten by **tsetse** fly . . .

    Definition: _____

    Sentence: _____

    _____

4. She rolled again and waited in **amazement**.

    Definition: _____

    Sentence: _____

    _____

5. . . . their excitement slowly turned to relief, and then **exhaustion**.

    Definition: _____

    Sentence: _____

    _____

6. Judy **shrugged** her shoulders . . .

    Definition: _____

    Sentence: _____

    _____

JUMANJI

1. Who are the main characters in the story? _____

   _____

2. What is their problem? _____

   _____

3. How do they solve it? _____

   _____

4. State your opinion about the ending of the story. _____

   _____

   Why? _____

5. Is this story fact or fantasy? _____

6. Would you look for more books written by Chris Van Allsburg? _____

   Why? _____

7. What time of year does this story take place? _____

   _____

8. Why is it important to read directions carefully? _____

   _____

9. What would you do differently if you were to play JUMANJI? _____

   _____

10. How long do you think a whisker's length is? Draw it below.

ART PROJECT:
   Choose your favorite picture to copy.
   Read the book jacket about the artist's work before you begin.

   Materials Needed: white construction paper
                          charcoal sticks
                          fixative
                          bookholder

THE LITTLE HOUSE

Caldecott Medal: 1943   **Illustrator & Author: Virginia Burton**

VOCABULARY: Look up the bold-faced word in the dictionary. Write a definition. Use the word in a sentence of your own.

1. Way off in the **distance** she could see the lights of the city.

   Definition: _____

   Sentence: _____

   _____

2. . . . along came some **surveyors** . . .

   Definition: _____

   Sentence: _____

   _____

3. Pretty soon there was an **elevated** train.

   Definition: _____

   Sentence: _____

   _____

4. They hurried by without a **glance**.

   Definition: _____

   Sentence: _____

   _____

5. At first the little house was **frightened**.

   Definition: _____

   Sentence: _____

   _____

6. . . . **tenement** house . . .

   Definition: _____

   Sentence: _____

   _____

THE LITTLE HOUSE

QUESTIONS:

1. Why couldn't the house be sold for gold or silver? _____

   _____

2. What does the sentence, "She was just as good a house as ever underneath" mean?

   _____

   _____

3. Is the story real or imaginary? _____

   Why? _____

   _____

4. What happened to the little house as the years went by? _____

   _____

5. Explain the ending of the story. _____

   _____

   _____

6. Does this story cover many years or just a few? _____

   _____

ART PROJECT:
   Choose your favorite picture from the book to copy.

   Materials Needed: white construction paper
   watercolors
   colored chalk
   felt pens
   fixative
   bookholder

   Directions: Notice the geometric shapes in the pictures (ovals, rectangles, etc.). Lay
                         your watercolors down in similar shapes.

Name _____

THE LITTLE ISLAND

Caldecott Medal: 1947   **Illustrator: Leonard Weishard**

VOCABULARY: Look up the bold-faced word in the dictionary. Write a definition. Use the word
in a sentence of your own.

1. And the **tides** rose and fell on the shore.

    Definition: _____

    Sentence: _____

    _____

2. Then one day all the **lobsters** crawled in from the sea.

    Definition: _____

    Sentence: _____

    _____

3. . . . and the gulls laid their eggs on the rocky **ledges**.

    Definition: _____

    Sentence: _____

    _____

4. The seaweed **squeaked** at low tide.

    Definition: _____

    Sentence: _____

    _____

5. "What's that?" said the cat — **"Faith."**

    Definition: _____

    Sentence: _____

    _____

THE LITTLE ISLAND

QUESTIONS:

1. Is this story real or imaginary? _____

   Why? _____

   _____

2. Why did the lobsters crawl up on land? _____

   _____

3. How does the little island shelter the animals? List the animals and tell how they receive shelter.

   _____

   _____

   _____

   _____

   _____

4. Explain how the kitten believed. _____

   _____

   Copy the exact sentence from the book to prove it. _____

   _____

   _____

5. How is the island a part of the world? _____

   _____

   _____

ART PROJECT:

Notice the author's color to express the changing seasons: fog, storms, day, night, and animals. Copy your favorite picture.

Materials Needed: white construction paper
watercolors
bookholder

LON PO PO

Caldecott Medal: 1990   **Illustrator: Ed Young**

VOCABULARY: Look up the bold-faced word in the dictionary. Write a definition. Use the word in a sentence of your own.

1. Close the door . . . and **latch** it well.

   Definition: _____

   Sentence: _____

   _____

2. . . . **disguised** as an old woman.

   Definition: _____

   Sentence: _____

   _____

3. She must have taken a different **route**.

   Definition: _____

   Sentence: _____

   _____

4. "Quickly open up" the **cunning** wolf said.

   Definition: _____

   Sentence: _____

   _____

5. The wolf . . . **paced** back and forth . . .

   Definition: _____

   Sentence: _____

   _____

6. . . . her bones have become **brittle**.

   Definition: _____

   Sentence: _____

   _____

LON PO PO

QUESTIONS:

1. How is the story of *Lon Po Po* different from the story of *Little Red Riding Hood*?

   _____

2. How did the wolf trick the children into letting him come in? _____

   _____

   _____

3. How did Shang figure out that there was a wolf in her bed? _____

   _____

   _____

4. Describe how Shang tricked the wolf. _____

   _____

   _____

   _____

   _____

5. What happened to the wolf when he almost touched the highest branch? _____

   _____

6. What art technique does the illustrator Ed Young use throughout the story? Compare this story
   to *Yeh-Shen* illustrated by Ed Young. _____

   _____

   _____

   _____

   _____

ART PROJECT:
Choose your favorite picture to copy.

Materials Needed: white construction paper   tissue to wipe chalk
                     colored chalk   fixative
                     charcoal sticks   bookholder

WRITING PROJECT:
Choose your favorite fairy tale and write a different version of it.

MADELINE'S RESCUE

Caldedcott Medal: 1954　　　　　　**Illustrator & Author: Ludwig Bemelmans**

VOCABULARY:　Look up the bold-faced word in the dictionary. Write a definition. Use the word in a sentence of your own.

1. When the first of May came near, there was **nervousness** each year.

   Definition: _____

   Sentence: _____

   _____

2. For on that day there arrived a collection of **trustees** for the . . .

   Definition: _____

   Sentence: _____

   _____

3. . . . the **annual** inspection.

   Definition: _____

   Sentence: _____

   _____

4. I mean — it's a perfect **disgrace**.

   Definition: _____

   Sentence: _____

   _____

5. You shall have your **vengeance**.

   Definition: _____

   Sentence: _____

   _____

6. The **gendarmes** said . . .

   Definition: _____

   Sentence: _____

   _____

MADELINE'S RESCUE

1. Where does this story take place? _____

_____

2. What kind of personality do you think the dog has? _____

_____

3. Why did Genevieve have to go? _____

_____

4. What happened so that the girls didn't fight over the dog? _____

_____

_____

5. The ending is called a surprise ending. How did it surprise you? _____

_____

_____

ART PROJECT:

Notice that the pictures are mainly yellow, black, and white. Choose your favorite picture to copy.

Materials Needed: white construction paper
watercolors
permanent black felt pen
white chalk
fixative
bookholder

Directions: Draw your picture first with a permanent black felt pen. Let dry. Watercolor over the ink. Fill in with white chalk.

Name _____

MAKE WAY FOR DUCKLINGS

Caldecott Medal: 1942   **Illustrator & Author: Robert McCloskey**

VOCABULARY: Look up the bold-faced word in the dictionary. Write a definition. Use the word in a sentence of your own.

1. . . . a strange **enormous** bird came by.

    Definition: _____

    Sentence: _____

    _____

2. . . . all in a **dither**.

    Definition: _____

    Sentence: _____

    _____

3. Mr. and Mrs. **Mallard** . . .

    Definition: _____

    Sentence: _____

    _____

4. It was a great **responsibility** taking care of so many ducklings.

    Definition: _____

    Sentence: _____

    _____

5. When at last she felt perfectly **satisfied** . . .

    Definition: _____

    Sentence: _____

    _____

T.S. Denison & Co., Inc./*Caldecott Activities*

MAKE WAY FOR DUCKLINGS

QUESTIONS:

1. What kind of feelings did you have for the Mallards as they walked through the city to get back to the public garden? _____

   _____

2. Who is Michael? _____

   _____

3. How does Michael help the Mallards? _____

   _____

4. What do you think might have happened to the Mallards without Michael's help in getting them to the park? _____

   _____

   _____

5. Why did the Mallards think the garden would be a good place to raise their family?

   _____

   _____

   _____

ART PROJECT:

Notice that Robert McCloskey worked only in brown and white, using clean lines and shading. The ducks are anatomically accurate. The pictures of Boston are historically correct for 1942.

Choose the picture you like best from the book to copy.

Materials Needed: white or tan construction paper
brown chalk or drawing pencils
tissue (use to rub chalk)
fixative
bookholder

Note: Robert McCloskey has another Caldecott Award winning book you might enjoy called *A Time of Wonder*.

Name _____

MANY MOONS

Caldecott Medal: 1944   **Illustrator: Louis Slobodkin**

VOCABULARY: Look up the bold-faced word in the dictionary. Write a definition. Use the word in a sentence of your own.

1. Once upon a time, in a **kingdom** by the sea . . .

   Definition: _____

   Sentence: _____

   _____

2. Lenore fell ill of a **surfeit** of raspberry tarts.

   Definition: _____

   Sentence: _____

   _____

3. He pulled a long scroll of **parchment** out.

   Definition: _____

   Sentence: _____

   _____

4. I have **conjured** up flowers . . .

   Definition: _____

   Sentence: _____

   _____

5. The **jester** came bounding into . . .

   Definition: _____

   Sentence: _____

   _____

6. . . . in his **motley** . . .

   Definition: _____

   Sentence: _____

   _____

MANY MOONS

QUESTIONS:

1. Is this story real or imaginary? _____

   Why? _____

   _____

2. What did Princess Lenore want? _____

   _____

3. Who helped Princess Lenore get what she wanted? _____

   _____

4. What was the moon for Lenore really made from?_____

   _____

5. How did Lenore explain the moon still being in the sky? _____

   _____

6. Why was the moon still shining? _____

   _____

ART PROJECT:
Choose your favorite picture from the book to copy.

Materials Needed: white construction paper
watercolors
tissue
black felt pen
colored chalk (blue, pink)
fixative
bookholder

Directions: Wet your drawing paper with clear water.
Paint your picture and dab paint with tissue while still wet.
When your picture is dry, outline it with pen and add detail.

MAY I BRING A FRIEND?

Caldecott Medal: 1965   **Illustrator: Beni Montresor**

VOCABULARY: Look up the bold-faced word in the dictionary. Write a definition. Use the word in a sentence of your own.

1. What **monkey business** is this?

    Definition: _____

    Sentence: _____

    _____

2. On Wednesday **morn** for breakfast . . .

    Definition: _____

    Sentence: _____

    _____

3. The queen said with a **frown** . . .

    Definition: _____

    Sentence: _____

    _____

QUESTIONS:

1. Who invited the boy to tea? _____

2. List the different friends he brought to tea. _____

    _____

    _____

3. What would you do if your were the King or Queen? _____

    _____

4. Were you surprised by the ending? _____

    Why? _____

    _____

    _____

ART PROJECT:
Choose your favorite picture from the book to copy.

Materials Needed: white and pink construction paper
                    black felt pen
                    bookholder

MEI LI

Caldecott Medal: 1939　　　　　　**Illustrator & Author: Thomas Handforth**

VOCABULARY:　Look up the bold-faced word in the dictionary. Write a definition. Use the word in a sentence of your own.

1. "I am going to take my lucky treasures and have **adventures** like . . ."
Definition: _____
Sentence: _____
_____

2. . . . one **lapis** blue . . .
Definition: _____
Sentence: _____
_____

3. . . . **scoffed** San Yo.
Definition: _____
Sentence: _____
_____

4. Her candle-top **swished** with vanity . . .
Definition: _____
Sentence: _____
_____

5. San Yu's **thrush** did not want to be left at home.
Definition: _____
Sentence: _____
_____

MEI LI

QUESTIONS:

1. What are girls expected to do in China when their brother goes to the fair? _____

   _____

   _____

2. Who went on the ice sled? _____

   _____

   _____

3. Do you think it was fortunate that Mei Li gave a lucky penny to Lidza? _____

   _____

   Why? _____

4. Why do you think the gates of the city are closed at night? _____

   _____

   _____

5. What are some of the different ways the pictures in the book show people traveling?

   _____

   _____

6. How did Mei Li spend her three pennies? _____

   _____

   _____

7. What were some dangerous things she did at the fair? _____

   _____

   _____

8. Write something you have done that might be considered dangerous. _____

   _____

   _____

ART PROJECT:
Choose the picture you like the best from the book to copy.

Materials Needed: white construction paper
charcoal sticks
thin black tempera & brush (to fill in picture)
fixative
bookholder

NINE DAYS TO CHRISTMAS

Caldecott Medal: 1960   **Illustrator: Marie Hall Ets**

VOCABULARY: Look up the bold-faced word in the dictionary. Write a definition. Use the word in a sentence of your own.

1. "And will I have a **pinata**?"
   Definition: _____
   Sentence: _____
   _____

2. "I wasn't **scolding**!"
   Definition: _____
   Sentence: _____
   _____

3. Pulling on the end of the rope that hung down by the **jacaranda** tree.
   Definition: _____
   Sentence: _____
   _____

4. . . . and the sound of children **scrambling** . . .
   Definition: _____
   Sentence: _____
   _____

QUESTIONS:

1. What country does this story take place in? _____
2. Explain the meaning of a posada. _____
   _____
3. What time of year is a posada held? _____
4. How many days does a posada last? _____
5. How old was Ceci? _____
6. Why was Ceci so excited? _____
   _____

7. Tell about a time you were excited for something to happen. _____

_____

_____

_____

_____

8. Describe Ceci's pinata. _____

_____

_____

9. Why was Ceci sad at her posada? _____

What made her happy again? _____

_____

10. How are the home and school in the story different from yours? _____

_____

_____

ART PROJECT:
Choose your favorite picture from the book to copy.

Materials Needed: gray or tan construction paper
pencil
thin black marker
colored chalk
fixative
bookholder

OPTIONAL ART ACTIVITY:
Make a pinata.

Materials Needed: balloon
newspaper torn in long strips
vano starch
poster paints

Directions: Blow up balloon.
Soak strips of newspaper in starch.
Layer over balloon to get the desired shape.
Let dry.
Paint.

Name _____

NOAH'S ARK

Caldecott Medal: 1978   **Illustrator: Peter Spier**

VOCABULARY: Look up the bold-faced word in the dictionary. Write a definition. Use the word in a sentence of your own.

1. Noah found **grace** in the eyes of the Lord.

   Definition: _____

   Sentence: _____

   _____

2. Wide and **stark**, was the ark.

   Definition: _____

   Sentence: _____

   _____

3. Noah's kin **clambered** in.

   Definition: _____

   Sentence: _____

   _____

4. All that walked, crawled or **stalked**.

   Definition: _____

   Sentence: _____

   _____

5. On dry earth found a **berth**.

   Definition: _____

   Sentence: _____

   _____

QUESTIONS:

1. Why did the Lord find grace in Noah? _____
_____

2. How did the animals come on board? _____

3. Why were the others killed? _____
_____
_____

4. What kind of jobs did Noah have on the ark? _____
_____

5. How did the ark become stranded? _____
_____

6. Why did Noah let a dove fly out the window? _____
_____

7. Why was Noah happy the dove brought back a twig? _____
_____

8. What happened to the rabbits and cats on the ark? _____
_____

9. What do you think the rainbow is a symbol of? _____
_____

10 .Suppose you could take Noah's place on the ark. How would you have felt? What do you think it would have been like living with all those animals on an ark? _____
_____
_____
_____

ART PROJECT:
Choose your favorite picture from the book to copy.

Materials Needed: white construction paper
watercolor
black felt pen
colored chalk
fixative
bookholder

ONCE A MOUSE

Caldecott Medal: 1962   **Illustrator: Marcia Brown**

VOCABULARY: Look up the bold-faced word in the dictionary. Write a definition. Use the word in a sentence of your own.

1. One day a **hermit** sat thinking about big and little.

   Definition: _____

   Sentence: _____

   _____

2. But the hermit was **mighty** at magic.

   Definition: _____

   Sentence: _____

   _____

3. Not long after that, a hungry tiger was **prowling** in the forest.

   Definition: _____

   Sentence: _____

   _____

4. . . . and with a **gesture** . . .

   Definition: _____

   Sentence: _____

   _____

5. The hermit missed nothing of all this, and **chided** the beast.

   Definition: _____

   Sentence: _____

   _____

6. You would be a **wretched** little mouse.

   Definition: _____

   Sentence: _____

   _____

7. The tiger felt **offended** . . .

   Definition: _____

   Sentence: _____

   _____

VOCABULARY: cont'd.

8. You are **ungrateful**.

Definition: _____

Sentence: _____

_____

QUESTIONS:

1. What was the hermit thinking of at the beginning of the book? _____

_____

2. Name the animals the hermit changed the mouse into. _____

_____

_____

3. How did the mouse's attitude change as he became larger? _____

_____

4. Why did the hermit change the tiger back to a mouse? _____

_____

5. What do you think happened to the mouse? _____

_____

ART PROJECT:

Look at the shapes of olive, red, and gold over-lapping to make the jungle undergrowth.
Choose your favorite picture from the book to copy.

Materials Needed: white construction paper   meat tray
blunt pencil   scissors
brayer   water soluble ink (in tube)
watercolors   marker pens
bookholder

Directions: Trim the curved edges from the meat tray.
Draw your design on the tray with a pencil.
Press hard to make the grooves deep.
Roll the colored ink over your picture.
Carefully place your picture face down on the construction paper.
Press down. Let your picture dry for one day.
Color in any parts you would like with watercolors or marker pens.

ONE FINE DAY

Caldecott Medal: 1972   **Illustrator: Nonny Hogrogian**

VOCABULARY: Look up the bold-faced word in the dictionary. Write a definition. Use the word in a sentence of your own.

1. . . . while she **gathered** wood for her fire.

   Definition: _____

   Sentence: _____

   _____

2. The cow **replied** . . .

   Definition: _____

   Sentence: _____

   _____

3. The fox found a fair **maiden**.

   Definition: _____

   Sentence: _____

   _____

4. So the fox found a **peddler** . . .

   Definition: _____

   Sentence: _____

   _____

5. . . . or the **cleverness** of the fox. . .

   Definition: _____

   Sentence: _____

   _____

6. **Sew** it in place. . .

   Definition: _____

   Sentence: _____

   _____

7. I'll trade you an egg for some **grain**.

   Definition: _____

   Sentence: _____

   _____

VOCABULARY: cont'd.

8. The fox was getting **desperate**. . .
   Definition: _____
   Sentence: _____
   _____

QUESTIONS:

1. *One Fine Day* is called a cumulative tale. What does "cumulative" mean? _____
   _____
   _____

   Name another tale that is cumulative. _____

2. Why did the fox have his tail cut off? _____
   _____

3. How did the fox get his tail sewn back on?_____
   _____

   List in order the things the fox had to get and whom he had to get them for.
   _____
   _____
   _____
   _____
   _____

4. How could the story have ended if the miller had not been kind?
   _____
   _____

ART PROJECT:
Copy your favorite picture from the book.

Materials Needed: white construction paper
                   watercolors
                   poster paint
                   tissue
                   bookholder

OWL MOON

Caldecott Medal: 1988   **Illustrator: John Schoenherr**

VOCABULARY: Look up the bold-faced word in the dictionary. Write a definition. Use the word in a sentence of your own.

1. The trees stood still as giant **statues**.

   Definition: _____

   Sentence: _____

   _____

2. And when their voices **faded** away. . .

   Definition: _____

   Sentence: _____

   _____

3. Pa **shrugged** and I shrugged.

   Definition: _____

   Sentence: _____

   _____

4. I was not **disappointed**.

   Definition: _____

   Sentence: _____

   _____

5. . . . we came to a **clearing** in the dark woods.

   Definition: _____

   Sentence: _____

   _____

6. Nothing in the **meadow** moved.

   Definition: _____

   Sentence: _____

   _____

OWL MOON

QUESTIONS:

1. Explain what it means to go owling. _____
   _____

2. Give 2 examples in which the author uses personification (gives human qualities to a lifeless
   thing or idea). _____
   _____
   _____
   _____
   _____

3. Why do you have to be brave when you go owling? _____
   _____
   _____

4. How would you feel staring at an owl for as long as a hundred minutes?
   _____

   Why? _____
   _____

5. What is the one thing that you need when you go owling? _____
   _____

6. Give 2 examples of similes (a statement saying one thing is like another).
   _____
   _____
   _____
   _____

ART PROJECT:
Choose your favorite picture from the book to copy.

Materials Needed: white construction paper
                         watercolors
                         charcoal
                         India ink
                         straw (blow India ink to look like bare branches)
                         pen to outline features

OX-CART MAN

Caldecott Medal: 1980   **Illustrator: Barbara Cooney**

VOCABULARY: Look up the bold-faced word in the dictionary. Write a definition. Use the word in a sentence of your own.

1. He packed a bag of wool he **sheared** from the sheep in April.

   Definition: _____

   Sentence: _____

   _____

2. He packed a **shawl** his wife wove on a loom.

   Definition: _____

   Sentence: _____

   _____

3. He packed linen made from **flax** he grew.

   Definition: _____

   Sentence: _____

   _____

4. He packed **shingles** he split himself.

   Definition: _____

   Sentence: _____

   _____

5. Then he sold his ox's yoke and **harness**.

   Definition: _____

   Sentence: _____

   _____

6. . . . his son took his Barlow knife and started **whittling**.

   Definition: _____

   Sentence: _____

   _____

OX-CART MAN

QUESTIONS:

1. In what season of the year does the story begin? _____

2. Why does the family work so hard all year? _____
   _____

3. Why do they start all over again the next year? _____
   _____

4. Why did the father go all the way to Portsmouth rather than stopping at one of the towns he
   walked through? _____
   _____

5. If you had been in this family, what would you have liked to do to help? _____
   _____
   _____

6. Do you think you would have liked to live then? _____
   Why? _____
   _____

7. How did you feel when the father sold the ox at Portsmouth? _____
   _____

8. Locate Portsmouth on a map of the United States. Give its location. _____
   _____

ART PROJECT:
Choose your favorite picture from the book to copy.

Materials Needed: white construction paper
poster paints
brush
water
bookholder

Neatly at the bottom of your picture, print the words on the page in black felt pen.

Name _____

THE POLAR EXPRESS

Caldecott Medal: 1986   **Author & Illustrator: Chris Van Allsburg**

VOCABULARY: Look up the bold-faced word in the dictionary. Write a definition. Use the word in a sentence of your own.

1. I did not **rustle** the sheets.

    Definition: _____

    Sentence: _____

    _____

2. . . . and ate candles with **nougat** centers.

    Definition: _____

    Sentence: _____

    _____

3. We crossed a **barren** desert of ice . . .

    Definition: _____

    Sentence: _____

    _____

4. . . . the train gave a sudden **lurch**. . .

    Definition: _____

    Sentence: _____

    _____

5. . . . cut a bell from a reindeer's **harness**.

    Definition: _____

    Sentence: _____

    _____

6. We traveled . . . where **lean** wolves roamed . . .

    Definition: _____

    Sentence: _____

    _____

THE POLAR EXPRESS

QUESTIONS:

1. What did the author mean by the statement, "It was wrapped in an apron of steam?"

   _____

   _____

2. What was the "barren dessert of ice"? _____

   _____

3. What gift did the boy ask for? _____

4. What gift would you have chosen if you were the boy? _____

   _____

5. What kind of person do you think the boy was? _____

   _____

6. Why couldn't the boy's parents hear the ringing of the bell? _____

   _____

   _____

7. Describe the colors used throughout the book. _____

   _____

ART PROJECT:
Choose your favorite picture to copy.

Art Materials: white construction paper
watercolors
colored chalk
poster paint
fixative
bookholder

Compare *The Polar Express* to *Jumanji*. Notice the pictures of the forest and the people. What kind of similarities do you see?

_____

_____

Name _____

PRAYER FOR A CHILD

Caldecott Medal: 1942   **Illustrator: Elizabeth Orton Jones**

VOCABULARY: Look up the bold-faced word in the dictionary. Write a definition. Use the word in a sentence of your own.

1. Wrapped in sweet **security**.

   Definition: _____

   Sentence: _____

   _____

2. Let no danger come to **fright**.

   Definition: _____

   Sentence: _____

   _____

3. My sleep . . . **beckons** at the window pane.

   Definition: _____

   Sentence: _____

   _____

4. Bless the hands that never **tire**.

   Definition: _____

   Sentence: _____

   _____

5. Keep them safe and free from **fear**.

   Definition: _____

   Sentence: _____

   _____

QUESTIONS:

1. Tell about a time you might have been afraid to go to bed. _____
    _____
    _____

2. What does it mean to be wrapped in sweet security? _____
    _____
    _____

3. Describe a special time with your mother. _____
    _____
    _____

4. How can toys make you feel safe? _____
    _____
    _____

5. Whose hands never tire of taking care of you? _____
    _____
    _____

6. How are your friends and family important to you? _____
    _____
    _____

7. What do you take to bed with you to make you feel safe? _____
    _____
    _____

8. Tell about a time you said a prayer before you went to sleep. How did it make you feel?
    _____
    _____
    _____

ART PROJECT:
Choose your favorite picture to copy.

Materials Needed: white construction paper   fixative
felt pen   bookholder
colored chalk

WRITING PROJECT:
Write a poem telling what you are thankful for.

Name _____

THE ROOSTER CROWS

Caldecott Medal: 1946   **Illustrators: Maud & Miska Petersham**

List three of your favorite rhymes.

1. _____

_____

_____

2. _____

_____

_____

3. _____

_____

_____

Many of these rhymes are to be used with jump ropes or hand rhythms.
Choose one, learn it, and then teach it to someone else.
Show it to your teacher.

ART PROJECT:
   Materials Needed: white construction paper
                        watercolors
                        black felt pen
                        bookholder

   Directions: Choose your favorite rhyme.
                        Carefully copy it on white paper with a thin black marker.
                        Using watercolor, paint the picture that goes with the rhyme.

SAINT GEORGE AND THE DRAGON

Caldecott Medal: 1985   **Illustrator: Trina Schart Hyman**

VOCABULARY: Look up the bold-faced word in the dictionary. Write a definition. Use the word in a sentence of your own.

1. The Red Cross Knight had never yet faced a **foe.**

   Definition: _____

   Sentence: _____

   _____

2. . . . as if she had a hidden **sorrow** in her heart.

   Definition: _____

   Sentence: _____

   _____

3. . . . where a good old **hermit** lived . . .

   Definition: _____

   Sentence: _____

   _____

4. The **wrathful** beast. . .

   Definition: _____

   Sentence: _____

   _____

5. Then they heard a **hideous** roaring . . .

   Definition: _____

   Sentence: _____

   _____

6. . . . and he was furious for **revenge.**

   Definition: _____

   Sentence: _____

   _____

SAINT GEORGE AND THE DRAGON

QUESTIONS:

1. Is the story real or imaginary? _____

   Explain why. _____

   _____

2. What was St. George's task? _____

   _____

3. Who was Una? _____

4. What story did the hermit tell the knight about the knight's childhood? _____

   _____

   _____

   _____

5. The knight fell twice in battle. What 2 things revived him so that he could fight the next day?

   1) _____

   2) _____

6. Why do you think Una wears black until the end of the book? _____

   _____

   _____

7. Who was the dragonslayer? _____

   _____

ART PROJECT:

Choose your favorite picture. Paint a watercolor landscape. Dry. Draw picture with felt pen. Color in areas with chalk as desired.

Materials Needed: white construction paper
watercolors
felt pen
colored chalk
fixative
bookholder

ADDITIONAL ACTIVITY:

Make 2 puppets: 1 — St. George
                          2 — the dragon
Tell the story of the battle.

Materials Needed: 2 paper bags
colored construction paper

SAM, BANGS & MOONSHINE

Caldecott Medal: 1967   **Illustrator & Author: Evaline Ness**

VOCABULARY: Look up the bold-faced word in the dictionary. Write a definition. Use the word in a sentence of your own.

1. She said the ragged old rug on the doorstep was a **chariot** drawn by dragons . . .
   Definition: _____
   Sentence: _____
   _____

2. She was so busy thinking that she was **unaware** of thick muddy clouds. . .
   Definition: _____
   Sentence: _____
   _____

3. Nor did she hear the **menacing** rumble of thunder.
   Definition: _____
   Sentence: _____
   _____

4. The **murky** light in the room deepened to black.
   Definition: _____
   Sentence: _____
   _____

5. Sam opened her eyes to see an **incredible** thing!
   Definition: _____
   Sentence: _____
   _____

6. "It's a **gerbil**."
   Definition: _____
   Sentence: _____
   _____

SAM, BANGS & MOONSHINE

QUESTIONS:

1. Explain the meaning of "moonshine" in this book. _____

   _____

2. Why did Thomas go to Blue Rock? _____

   _____

3. What happened to Bangs? _____

   _____

4. Explain how Thomas was saved. _____

   _____

   _____

5. Explain the lesson Sam learned in this story. _____

   _____

   _____

6. Why was it important that she learned this lesson? _____

   _____

   _____

7. Compare Sam with someone you know in real life. Tell how you felt when that person used
   "moonshine" with you. _____

   _____

   _____

   _____

ART PROJECT:
Study the muted green, brown, and gray washes, as well as the use of black lines to give a misty foggy feeling. Choose your favorite picture from the book to copy.

Materials Needed: white construction paper
charcoal sticks
colored chalk
fixative
bookholder

SHADOW

Caldecott Medal: 1983   **Illustrator: Marcia Brown**

VOCABULARY: Look up the bold-faced word in the dictionary. Write a definition. Use the word in a sentence of your own.

1. It goes forth at night to **prowl** around the fires.

   Definition: _____

   Sentence: _____

   _____

2. It even likes to mingle with the **dancers**.

   Definition: _____

   Sentence: _____

   _____

3. But it is **mute**.

   Definition: _____

   Sentence: _____

4. . . . stirring the **embers**.

   Definition: _____

   Sentence: _____

   _____

5. . . . it reaches for a **perch**.

   Definition: _____

   Sentence: _____

   _____

6. . . . of all the **squirms**.

   Definition: _____

   Sentence: _____

   _____

SHADOW

QUESTIONS:

1. Read the introduction of this book. Where does this story take place? _____

   _____

2. What is a "shaman"? _____

   _____

3. What are some things a shadow does not have that are specifically mentioned in this book?

   _____

   _____

4. What does this mean: "The eye has no shadow, but it sees Shadow stirring the embers"?

   _____

   _____

   _____

5. Why is Shadow blind? _____

   _____

6. Compare this book to *Ashanti to Zulu* and *Why Mosquitos Buzz in People's Ears*. What
   similarities do you see? _____

   _____

7. Why is Shadow a trickster? _____

   _____

ART PROJECT:
Choose your favorite picture from the book to copy.
Use a watercolor background. Cut figures from construction paper. Arrange with tissue paper.

Materials Needed: white construction paper   colored paper
                       watercolors   white tissue paper

SCIENCE PROJECT:
Study your shadow.
Measure it at different times of the day, at 9:00 a.m. _____ at noon _____
at 3:00 p.m. _____

When is it longest? _____ shortest? _____

Why does the direction of your shadow change? _____

RESEARCH:
Read about shadows in an encyclopedia. Write a short report.

THE SNOWY DAY

Caldecott Medal: 1963   **Illustrator: Ezra Jack Keats**

VOCABULARY: Look up the bold-faced word in the dictionary. Write a definition. Use the word in a sentence of your own.

1. **Crunch**, crunch, crunch, his feet sank in the snow.

   Definition: _____

   Sentence: _____

   _____

2. . . . a stick that was just right for **smacking** a snow-covered tree.

   Definition: _____

   Sentence: _____

   _____

3. Then he **dragged** his feet s-l-o-w-l-y to make tracks.

   Definition: _____

   Sentence: _____

   _____

4. After breakfast he put on his **snowsuit** . . .

   Definition: _____

   Sentence: _____

   _____

5. . . . and he made **angels**.

   Definition: _____

   Sentence: _____

   _____

6. He **pretended** he was a mountain climber.

   Definition: _____

   Sentence: _____

   _____

7. . . . and he **thought** and thought and thought about them.

   Definition: _____

   Sentence: _____

   _____

THE SNOWY DAY

QUESTIONS:

1. What kinds of tracks did Peter make in the snow? _____
   _____
   _____

2. How did he know he wasn't old enough to join the big boys in their snowball fight? _____
   _____
   _____

3. List several things Peter did instead. _____
   _____
   _____
   _____
   _____

4. Explain why Peter's dream was or was not true. _____
   _____

5. Where do you think Peter lives? _____
   _____

6. About how old would you guess Peter is? _____

7. What did you think was going to happen to Peter's snowball? _____
   _____

8. Why didn't Peter know what happened to his snowball? _____
   _____

ART PROJECT:

Make a collage of your favorite picture from the book.

Materials Needed: colored construction paper
   glue
   scissors
   collage box materials (wallpaper, toothbrush, cotton, tissue paper, etc.)
   bookholder

If you enjoyed this book about Peter, Ezra Jack Keats has written several more about Peter. They are:

   Peter's Chair
   Whistle For Willie
   A Letter to Amy

Name _____

SONG AND DANCE MAN

Caldecott Medal: 1989   **Illustrator: Stephen Gammell**

VOCABULARY: Look up the bold-faced word in the dictionary. Write a definition. Use the word
in a sentence of your own.

1. . . . danced on the **vaudeville** stage.

Definition: _____

Sentence: _____

_____

2. . . . **gliding** across a vaudeville stage.

Definition: _____

Sentence: _____

_____

3. It's the grand **finale**.

Definition: _____

Sentence: _____

_____

4. . . . wraps them gently in the **shammy** cloth.

Definition: _____

Sentence: _____

_____

5. Grandpa **glances** back up the stairs.

Definition: _____

Sentence: _____

_____

SONG AND DANCE MAN

QUESTIONS:

1. What kind of entertainment did people have before T.V.? _____
_____

2. Where did Grandpa take his grandchildren while he was waiting for supper? _____
_____

3. Why does Grandpa sprinkle powder on the dance floor? _____
_____
_____

4. Name 4 things Grandpa does to entertain the children.
   1) _____
   2) _____
   3) _____
   4) _____

5. Why does Grandpa say he wouldn't trade a million "good old" days for the days he spends with the children? _____
_____

ART PROJECT:
Choose your favorite picture to copy.

Materials Needed: white construction paper   tissue
colored chalk   fixative
colored pencils   bookholder
charcoal sticks

Directions: Notice the use of pastels throughout the book. Using colored chalk, rub desired colors on the edge of a piece of construction paper. Hold on top of paper that you want to transfer it on to. Using a tissue, rub colors from one piece of construction paper to the one your picture will be on. Draw figures with charcoal sticks. Add lines with colored pencils.

WRITING PROJECT:
Write a story telling about a special thing your grandpa likes to do with you.

Name _____

SONG OF THE SWALLOWS

Caldecott Medal: 1950   **Illustrator & Author: Leo Politi**

VOCABULARY: Look up the bold-faced word in the dictionary. Write a definition. Use the word in a sentence of your own.

1. The bells of the **mission** church. . .

   Definition: _____

   Sentence: _____

   _____

2. . . . and the **barracks** for the soldiers.

   Definition: _____

   Sentence: _____

   _____

3. . . . they grew strong and bore bright, **fragrant** flowers.

   Definition: _____

   Sentence: _____

   _____

4. . . . and the mission gardens became quieter and more **subdued**.

   Definition: _____

   Sentence: _____

   _____

5. . . . when the mission **reigned** supreme. . .

   Definition: _____

   Sentence: _____

   _____

6. . . . they were so clumsy and **awkward**!

   Definition: _____

   Sentence: _____

   _____

SONG OF THE SWALLOWS

QUESTIONS:

1. Where does the story take place? _____
_____

2. When do the swallows return each year? _____

3. What did Juan and Julian do when they spotted the first swallows? _____
_____
_____

4. Is this story real or imaginary? _____

   Why? _____
_____

5. Why did Juan want swallows to nest at his home? _____
_____
_____

ART PROJECT:
Choose your favorite picture from the book to copy.

Materials Needed: white construction paper
watercolors
colored chalk
black felt pen
colored chalk
fixative
bookholder

RESEARCH:
Read about Mission San Juan Capistrano. Write a paper telling about the history of the mission.

Name _____

A STORY-A STORY

Caldecott Medal: 1971   **Illustrator: Gail E. Haley**

VOCABULARY: Look up the bold-faced word in the dictionary. Write a definition. Use the word in a sentence of your own.

1. Next Ananse cut a **frond** from a banana tree . . .

   Definition: _____

   Sentence: _____

   _____

2. . . . and filled a **calabash** with water.

   Definition: _____

   Sentence: _____

   _____

3. He sat the little doll at the foot of a **flamboyant** tree.

   Definition: _____

   Sentence: _____

   _____

4. . . . and she was **furious**.

   Definition: _____

   Sentence: _____

   _____

QUESTIONS:

1. What country does this story come from? _____

2. Is the story real or imaginary? _____

   Why? _____

   _____

3. How does Ananse get up to the Sky God?_____

   _____

4. What price does the Sky God ask for the stories? _____

   _____

   _____

5. What clever tricks does Ananse use to catch the three things for the Sky God?

_____

_____

_____

_____

6. How did the Sky God feel when Ananse brought him his price? _____

_____

_____

Tell about a time when you felt this way. _____

_____

_____

_____

_____

7. How did the stories scatter to all corners of the world? _____

_____

8. Why do you think the world needs stories? _____

_____

_____

ART PROJECT:

Choose your favorite picture from the book to copy.

Materials Needed: meat tray (styrofoam)
white construction paper
brayer
water soluble ink (in tube)
pencil
scissors
colored markers
bookholder

Directions: Trim curved edges from meat tray.
Draw picture with dull pencil onto tray. Press hard.
Roll colored ink onto picture on tray.
Press tray down on white construction paper. Press hard.
Dry and fill in with colored markers.

SYLVESTER AND THE MAGIC PEBBLE

Caldecott Medal: 1970   **Illustrator & Author: William Steig**

VOCABULARY: Look up the bold-faced word in the dictionary. Write a definition. Use the word in a sentence of your own.

1. On a rainy Saturday during vacation he found a quite **extraordinary** one.
   Definition: _____
   Sentence: _____
   _____

2. It **ceased**.
   Definition: _____
   Sentence: _____
   _____

3. In all his young life Sylvester had never had a wish **gratified** so quickly.
   Definition: _____
   Sentence: _____
   _____

4. . . . and he wished a wart on his left hind **fetlock** would disappear.
   Definition: _____
   Sentence: _____
   _____

5. . . . and went away confused, **perplexed**, puzzled, and bewildered.
   Definition: _____
   Sentence: _____
   _____

6. . . . into every nook and **gully** of the neighborhood and beyond.
   Definition: _____
   Sentence: _____
   _____

SYLVESTER AND THE MAGIC PEBBLE

QUESTIONS:

1. What did the Duncan family feel was the most important thing for them? _____
   _____

2. Would you have changed the ending? _____

   Why? _____
   _____

3. Was this story real or imaginary? _____

   Why? _____
   _____

4. Why did Sylvester choose to sleep when he was a rock? _____
   _____

5. Why did life have no meaning for the Duncan's without Sylvester? _____
   _____
   _____

6. Tell about a time you might have felt like this. _____
   _____
   _____
   _____

ART PROJECT:
   Choose your favorite picture to copy.

   Materials Needed: construction paper   colored chalk
                        poster paint   black felt pen
                        brush   fixative
                        water   bookholder

WRITING PROJECT:
   If you were holding a magic pebble, write about what you would wish and how it would change
   your life. Use white lined paper.

THEY WERE STRONG AND GOOD

Caldecott Medal: 1941   **Illustrator & Author: Robert Lawson**

VOCABULARY: Look up the bold-faced word in the dictionary. Write a definition. Use the word in a sentence of your own.

1. They went down to the **wharves** to sell things . . .

    Definition: _____

    Sentence: _____

    _____

2. They would **stalk** into the kitchen . . .

    Definition: _____

    Sentence: _____

    _____

3. They sent her to a **convent** to go to school.

    Definition: _____

    Sentence: _____

    _____

4. . . . he was **pursued** by deserters.

    Definition: _____

    Sentence: _____

    _____

5. . . . so they made him a **guidon** bearer.

    Definition: _____

    Sentence: _____

    _____

6. There were **lumberjacks** there too.

    Definition: _____

    Sentence: _____

    _____

QUESTIONS:

1. Is this story real or imaginary? _____

   Why? _____

   _____

2. Look up the word **autobiography**. What does it mean? _____

   _____

3. Who were the people the author told you about? _____

   _____

   _____

4. What happened to the author's relatives during the Civil War? _____

   _____

   _____

5. Locate **Minnesota** on a map of the United States. Give its location. _____

   _____

   _____

6. What is a deserter? _____

   _____

ART PROJECT:
Choose your favorite picture from the book to copy.

Materials Needed: white construction paper
                     charcoal
                     fixative
                     bookholder

EXTRA ACTIVITY:
Draw the author's family tree on a piece of white drawing paper.

RESEARCH:
Ask your parents or grandparents to tell you a story about their past that you might find interesting. Share it with the class. Draw your own family tree.

TIME OF WONDER

Caldecott Medal: 1958   **Illustrator: Robert McCloskey**

VOCABULARY: Look up the bold-faced word in the dictionary. Write a definition. Use the word in a sentence of your own.

1. Slowly **unfurling** . . .

   Definition: _____

   Sentence: _____

   _____

2. . . . making salty young **silhouettes**.

   Definition: _____

   Sentence: _____

   _____

3. Their **reflections** gazing up . . .

   Definition: _____

   Sentence: _____

   _____

4. . . . **battening** down.

   Definition: _____

   Sentence: _____

   _____

5. You awaken to an **unaccustomed** light.

   Definition: _____

   Sentence: _____

   _____

6. . . . **migrating** birds from the north . . .

   Definition: _____

   Sentence: _____

   _____

QUESTIONS:

1. What were the people getting ready for? _____

   _____

2. What do you notice about the words and spacing that McCloskey uses? _____

   _____

   _____

3. How does the storm begin? _____

   _____

4. List some of the damage caused by the hurricane. _____

   _____

   _____

5. What showed the age of the shells at the Indian shell heap? _____

   _____

6. During what season did the story take place? _____

7. What kind of feeling do you sense at the end of the story? _____

   _____

   Explain. _____

   _____

ART PROJECT:
Notice that Mr. McCloskey used a lot of blue and green in his pictures.
Choose your favorite picture from the book to copy.

Materials Needed: white construction paper
                    watercolors
                    book holder

A TREE IS NICE

Caldecott Medal: 1957   **Illustrator: Marc Simont**

VOCABULARY: Look up the bold-faced word in the dictionary. Write a definition. Use the word in a sentence of your own.

1. We build **playhouses** out of the leaves.

   Definition: _____

   Sentence: _____

   _____

2. Then we pile them up with our rakes and have a **bonfire**.

   Definition: _____

   Sentence: _____

   _____

3. The leaves whisper in the **breeze** all summer long.

   Definition: _____

   Sentence: _____

   _____

4. A tree is nice because it has a trunk and **limbs**.

   Definition: _____

   Sentence: _____

   _____

5. Or play **pirate** ship up in the tree.

   Definition: _____

   Sentence: _____

   _____

6. It is a good place to lean your **hoe** while we rest.

   Definition: _____

   Sentence: _____

   _____

QUESTIONS:

1. List 3 reasons the author said a tree was nice.

   1) _____

   2) _____

   3) _____

2. What does the author say that people will feel about a tree? _____

   _____

3. How can a tree protect a house? _____

   _____

   _____

4. How do you feel when you see a tree? _____

   _____

5. Tell how some trees could make you feel different from others. _____

   _____

   _____

6. Explain the proper way to plant a tree. Check your encyclopedia. _____

   _____

   _____

   _____

7. How does a tree begin its growth? _____

8. Notice the pictures throughout the book. How does the illustrator use contrast?

   _____

   _____

ART PROJECT:
Choose your favorite picture to copy.
Include the writing on the page you copy.

Materials Needed: white construction paper
watercolors
thin black marker (permanent)
bookholder

Directions: Outline trees in a permanent black felt pen.
Let dry. Fill in with watercolor.

WHERE THE WILD THINGS ARE

Caldecott Medal: 1964   **Illustrator: Maurice Sendak**

VOCABULARY: Look up the bold-faced word in the dictionary. Write a definition. Use the word in a sentence of your own.

1. The night Max wore his wolf suit and made **mischief** of one kind and another.

   Definition: _____

   Sentence: _____

   _____

2. . . . and an ocean **tumbled** by with a private boat for Max . . .

   Definition: _____

   Sentence: _____

   _____

3. . . . they roared their **terrible** roars . . .

   Definition: _____

   Sentence: _____

   _____

4. . . . and **gnashed** their terrible teeth . . .

   Definition: _____

   Sentence: _____

   _____

5. . . . and they were **frightened** and called him the most wild thing of all.

   Definition: _____

   Sentence: _____

   _____

6. . . . "let the wild **rumpus** start!" . . .

   Definition: _____

   Sentence: _____

   _____

WHERE THE WILD THINGS ARE

QUESTIONS:

1. What kind of mischief did Max get into? _____

   _____

2. How did Max tame the monsters? _____

   _____

3. Why did Max return home? _____

   _____

4. How long was Max really gone? _____

   _____

5. What do you think really happened to Max? _____

   _____

6. What kind of person was Max? _____

   Copy a sentence from the story to prove your statement. _____

   _____

   _____

7. Compare Max with some person you know quite well. Tell one way in which they are alike and
   one way in which they are different.

   ALIKE: _____

   _____

   DIFFERENT: _____

   _____

ART PROJECT:
Choose your favorite picture from the book to copy.

Materials Needed: lined writing paper   watercolors
                 white paper   colored chalk
                 pencil   fixative
                 felt pen   bookholder

WRITING ACTIVITY:
Write a story about your own wild thing. Remember to tell "who?," "what?," "when?," "where?,"
and "why?" in your story. Illustrate your own wild thing on a piece of paper.

WHITE SNOW, BRIGHT SNOW

Caldecott Medal: 1948   **Illustrator: Roger Duvoisin**

VOCABULARY: Look up the bold-faced word in the dictionary. Write a definition. Use the word in a sentence of your own.

1. . . . the rabbits knew it, and **scurried** around . . .

   Definition: _____

   Sentence: _____

   _____

2. . . . whispering quietly as they **shifted** down.

   Definition: _____

   Sentence: _____

   _____

3. . . . the rabbits hid in their warm **burrows** . . .

   Definition: _____

   Sentence: _____

   _____

4. . . . buried in **snowdrifts** . . .

   Definition: _____

   Sentence: _____

   _____

5. Houses **crouched** together . . .

   Definition: _____

   Sentence: _____

   _____

6. . . . looking for the snowdrops and **crocuses** that grew there.

   Definition: _____

   Sentence: _____

   _____

WHITE SNOW, BRIGHT SNOW

QUESTIONS:

1. List 4 ways people knew the snow was coming.

    1)_____
    2)_____
    3)_____
    4)_____

2. Tell 4 things the children did when it snowed.

    1)_____
    2)_____
    3)_____
    4)_____

3. Where did the rabbits go when it snowed?_____
   _____

4. What did the policeman's wife do for him? _____
   _____

5. Explain what a mustard plaster is.
   _____
   _____

6. How did the children know that Spring had really come? _____
   _____

ART PROJECT:
Choose your favorite picture from the book to copy.

Materials Needed: gray construction paper
poster paint
bookholder

Directions: Paint on gray paper.

Name _____

WHY MOSQUITOES BUZZ IN PEOPLE'S EARS

Caldecott Medal: 1976   **Illustrators: Leo & Diane Dillon**

VOCABULARY: Look up the bold-faced word in the dictionary. Write a definition. Use the word in a sentence of your own.

1. One morning a mosquito saw an **iguana** . . .

   Definition: _____

   Sentence: _____

   _____

2. They came and sat down . . . around a **council** fire.

   Definition: _____

   Sentence: _____

   _____

3. . . . who came **slithering** . . .

   Definition: _____

   Sentence: _____

   _____

4. . . . and I thought he was **plotting** some mischief against me.

   Definition: _____

   Sentence: _____

   _____

5. The antelope was sent to **fetch** him.

   Definition: _____

   Sentence: _____

   _____

6. . . . who **annoyed** the iguana.

   Definition: _____

   Sentence: _____

   _____

WHY MOSQUITOES BUZZ IN PEOPLE'S EARS

QUESTIONS:

1. Is the story real or imaginary? _____

   Why? _____

2. Why did the iguana put sticks in his ears? _____

   _____

3. List the 6 main animals as they are introduced in the story. Tell what each does.

   1) _____

   2) _____

   3) _____

   4) _____

   5) _____

   6) _____

4. Why won't Mother Owl wake the sun? _____

   _____

5. Whose fault did the council think it was? _____

   _____

6. Why do you think mosquitoes buzz in people's ears? _____

   _____

   _____

ART PROJECT:

Choose your favorite picture to copy.

Materials Needed: meat tray (styrofoam)   watercolors
                    brayer   colored pencils
                    water soluble ink (in tube)   white construction paper
                    black felt pen   colored markers
                                                   bookholder

Directions: Cut edges from meat tray. With a dull pencil, deeply draw your picture. Using brayer, spread ink over picture etched in meat tray. Place on white paper to print. When your print is dry, fill in the rest of the colors between the printed lines, using watercolors or marker pens.

Note: The illustrators have received another Caldecott Medal for their book *From Ashanti to Zulu.* You might enjoy comparing the two books.

Cooperative Learning

The following exercise is designed to be used by teachers who wish to study the Caldecott books cooperatively. Sample questions which are intended for cooperative interaction are given for **Where the Wild Things Are**; **Sam, Bangs & Moonshine**; and **The Snowy Day** (found on the following three pages). These are presented as sample formats which can be applied to any of the other stories found in *Caldecott Activities*. These sample questions are easily derived from the "Questions" sections seen on pages 6–107. The following materials are needed for a class of 32 students: eight books of one title, eight worksheets, eight pencils, eight groups of students of four, and large chart paper for the teacher to record children's answers.

For each group of four children, there should be one runner, one recorder, one reader, and one speaker. The duties of each child are as follows:

Runner	Gets Caldecott book from teacher and takes book back to group. Gives book to reader.
Reader	Reads story to group. If the child tires of reading, another child may read, or the story may be read by different members of the group. (The *Reader* should also **show** the pictures to the other children.)
Runner	Takes book back to the teacher and picks up worksheet with questions. Gives worksheet to the recorder.
Recorder	Writes down answers from the group. The group may come up with several possible answers for each question. When all questions have been answered, the group must decide on the correct answer to each question and circle it. The Recorder then gives the paper to the Speaker.
Speaker	Gives the group's agreed—upon answer to the teacher who records answers on a large piece of chart paper.

This lesson may take up to two hours to complete depending on the age group of the students. The purpose of this lesson is to allow children to think of as many solutions as possible. This allows the teacher to see different types of deduction. Because the children do not get to look through the book for the answers, they must rely on each other's memory for helping. The children also have better retention of the reading material because they are collaborating.

As a follow-up activity to the reading, the children do an art project that goes along with the story. They may choose any picture from the book or use an idea from their own imagination. (*Note: Explained art activities are seen on pages 6–107.*)

WHERE THE WILD THINGS ARE

by Maurice Sendak

Choose three possible answers for each question. Circle the number of the answer that everyone agrees on.

What kind of person is Max?

1. _____
2. _____
3. _____

How long was Max really gone?

1. _____
2. _____
3. _____

What do you think really happened to Max?

1. _____
2. _____
3. _____

How did Max get to where the wild things were?

1 _____
2. _____
3. _____

Why does Max return home?

1. _____
2. _____
3. _____

Each person must sign to show:

1. Agreement
2. Completion of the task

1. _____
2. _____
3. _____
4. _____

SAM, BANGS & MOONSHINE

by Evaline Ness

Choose three possible answers for each question. Circle the number of the answer that everyone agrees on.

What is" moonshine"?

1. _____
2. _____
3. _____

What kind of a person is Thomas?

1. _____
2. _____
3. _____

How did Sam feel when she heard thunder?

1. _____
2. _____
3. _____

What important lesson did Sam learn?

1. _____
2. _____
3. _____

Why do you think Sam used moonshine?

1. _____
2. _____
3. _____

Each person must sign to show:

   1. Agreement
   2. Completion of the task

1. _____
2. _____
3. _____
4. _____

THE SNOWY DAY

by Ezra Jack Keets

Choose three possible answers for each question. Circle the number of the answer that you all agree on.

What did Peter do when he woke up?

1. _____
2. _____
3. _____

Where do you think Peter lives?

1. _____
2. _____
3. _____

What kind of tracks did Peter make?

1. _____
2. _____
3. _____

How did Peter know he wasn't old enough to join the big boys in their snowball fight?

1. _____
2. _____
3. _____

Why didn't Peter know what happened to his snowball?

1. _____
2. _____
3. _____

Each person must sign to show:

1. Agreement
2. Completion of the task

1. _____
2. _____
3. _____
4. _____

LESSONS FOR TEACHING CALDECOTTS IN A WHOLE LANGUAGE PROGRAM

The following instructions are designed to be used by teachers who wish to study the Caldecott books within a whole language context. Sample format pages are given for **The Little House**; **Owl Moon**; and **Sam, Bangs & Moonshine** (found on the following three pages).

Acquainting students with the illustrators and writers of children's books, allowing them to respond to the story through quickwrites, pair/share, read arounds, character analysis charts, as well as copying their favorite picture through the use of a variety of art media are some of the best ways to get children "hooked" on reading. The following strategies are examples of how a teacher may use the Caldecott Medal Award Books to take students into, through, and beyond a story. (The teacher may use one book, 15 books for partners, or 30 books for a whole class; depending on the availability of books.)

Discussion of the illustrator's or writer's life is very beneficial to help the student see a connection between life's experiences, art, and writing. It serves as a model for children to start collecting their own portfolios of pictures, or writing down ideas in a journal for their own stories.

A **quickwrite** is a strategy in which children write for five minutes on a given topic. Using a response journal or a piece of paper, they may either respond to a topic to get them into the story or to a statement from the book. Tell the children they are to *remain in their desks*—they may not come to you with questions during the quickwrite period. If the children get writer's block instruct them to keep their pencils moving by *writing down* "I'm stuck," or "I don't know what to write," or anything else that comes into their heads until an idea pops into their minds. This procedure helps to free up ideas. The teacher should write along with the students and share his/her ideas with the class.

A **read around** is a strategy in which each child in a group of four reads his/her quickwrite to the other children. The children may respond to each other's ideas.

In **pair/share** each student turns to a partner and reads his/her quickwrite. They share their ideas with one another. The teacher may elect to have volunteers share their idea with the whole class.

Character analysis charts may be used to record ideas about the personality traits of a character. The teacher may either read the book aloud or show a video of the book. As the children listen to the story, they record their ideas on a piece of paper. These ideas are used later for an additional writing assignment such as writing a thesis statement about a character. The children reread the book on their own using a dialectical journal to find evidence about a chosen character to prove their "thesis."

A **dialectical journal** is a paper folded in half. On the left side of the paper the student writes a statement. On the right side of the paper the student writes down evidence from the book along with the page number to support the statement on the left.

Children may then choose their favorite picture from the book to copy using similar art media used by the illustrator.

THE LITTLE HOUSE
by Virginia Lee Burton

Theme: Story of change—The further away we get from nature and the simple ways of life, the less happy we are. Virginia Burton's story conveys the idea of urbanization after a century of a city's growth (development the transportation, of paved streets, and reinforced concrete buildings). The heroine of story is the little house. Although its surroundings change, the house is stationary until the end of story (historical perspective).

INTO

Quickwrite (or discuss): Notice the picture on the book cover. What do you think this story is about?

Read Around or Pair/Share: Students read their quickwrites aloud to a partner or group.

Discuss: Teacher should discuss Virginia Lee Burton and the 1943 Caldecott Award. Virginia Lee Burton wanted to be a dancer, but stayed home to care for her father. She was a perfectionist, and knew her own children were her best critics.

THROUGH

Teacher Reads Story (children may follow along)
Discuss or quickwrite: "She couldn't be sold for gold or silver." (p. 18.)

Teacher Reads Story (children may follow along)
Discuss or quickwrite: Tell about a time you might have felt like this little house. Everyone is hurrying around so fast they do not even notice you. (p. 26.)

Teacher Reads Story (children may follow along)
Discuss: "She looked shabby . . .. though she was just as good a house as ever underneath." (p. 31.)

BEYOND

Art: Notice the house; what do you see (face)? Think about the shapes in the picture. Use watercolor to recreate the scene.

Science: Nocturnal scenes every 4 or 5 pages spaces the bright colors and accentuates the flow of time.

Study: The rising and setting of the sun signifying
The passing of the hours of the day,
The waxing and waning of the moon,
The succession of the days of the month,
The rotation of the seasons,
The evanescence of the year.

OWL MOON

by Jane Yolen
illustrated by John Schoenherr

Theme: Relationship of a child and parent, and their special times in the woods.

INTO

Quickwrite (or discuss): Look at the cover of *Owl Moon*. How is the title significant? What picture do you visualize in your mind?

Read Around or *Pair/Share*: Students read their quickwrites aloud to a partner or group.

Discuss: Teacher should discuss John Schoenherr and the 1988 Caldecott Award. John Schoenherr wanted to be a painter of wildlife. He got his first job illustrating as a fill–in for another illustrator. He illustrated *Rascal*, *Gentle Ben*, *Julie of the Wolves*, and *Dune*. Schoenherr likes to use intuitive discovery in his art. This book was easy for him since all he had to do was walk outside in his own back woods to observe the trees, fields, buildings, walls, and snow. He illustrated this book in pen and watercolor.

Discuss: Similes and personification—prior lessons on these figures of speech should be taught to the class so there is some familiarity with them.

THROUGH

Teacher Reads Story (children may follow along)
   Listen for personification and similes.

Cooperative Groups: At the end of the story have children work in groups of 3–4 and chart both similes and personification found in the story.

Examples:

Personification	**Simile**
The moon made his face into a silver mask.	It was as quiet as a dream.
The little gray footprints followed us.	Trees stood still as giant statues.
The short round shadow bumped after me.	The train whistle blew like a sad, sad song.

BEYOND

Art: Paint a watercolor background. Using a charcoal stick or colored chalk, sketch in the trees, owl, and figures. India Ink may be blown on with a straw to create the branches of the trees.

Writing Activity: Write a story about a time you did something special with someone close to you, such as your father or a good friend.

SAM, BANGS & MOONSHINE
by Evaline Ness

Theme: Story illustrates both the childhood pain of losing a loved one plus the positive and negative effects of fantasy.

INTO

Quickwrite (or discuss): Tell about a time when you pretended something that was not really true.

Read Around or ***Pair/Share:*** Students read their quickwrites aloud to a partner or group.

Discuss: Teacher should discuss Evaline Ness and the 1967 Caldecott Award. Evaline Ness did not start drawing until high school .She went to art school at the Chicago Art Institute. Evaline Ness kept her drawings in a portfolio and referred to them for ideas later used in books. She used an ink roller and a wad of string for texture. Like Sam, she tells stories, but hers are put into books for children.

THROUGH

Teacher Reads Story (or shows video)
Children listen using a character analysis sheet. Students write down personality traits of each character.

Writing: Student chooses a character to write a thesis statement about. (Example: Thomas was very gullible.) The student then rereads the story again to find evidence to support the statement. This information is written into a paragraph. A concluding paragraph is then written to summarize the findings.

BEYOND

Art: Using charcoal and colored chalk, draw your favorite picture from the story. Spray with hairspray as a fixative.

Research: Research the use of a lighthouse in a harbor. Give an oral report on it to the class.

SAM, BANGS & MOONSHINE

by Evaline Ness

Directions: As you hear or view the story of *Sam, Bangs & Moonshine*, write down the character traits or personalities of each character.

CHARACTER ANALYSIS

CHARACTER   *PERSONALITY TRAITS*

SAM   _____

            _____

            _____

            _____

THOMAS   _____

            _____

            _____

            _____

BANGS   _____

            _____

            _____

            _____

FATHER   _____

            _____

            _____

            _____

DIALECTICAL JOURNAL

SENTENCES OR PHRASES I LIKE	QUESTIONS, COMMENTS I HAVE

BOOKHOLDER PATTERN AND INSTRUCTIONS

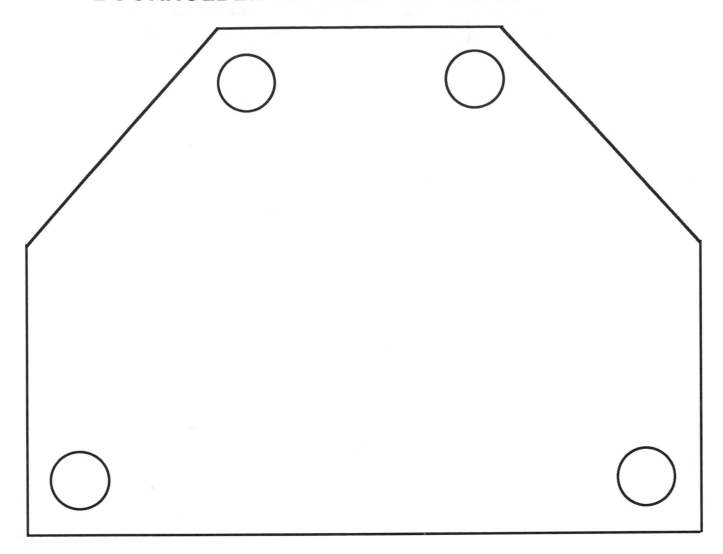

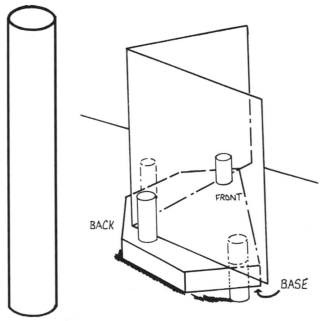

BACK

FRONT

BASE

Materials:
1/2" thick piece of wood (5" x 7 1/2")
4–1/2" x 3" pieces of dowling
drill
glue

Directions:
The bookholder will consist of a 1/2 inch piece of wood approximately 5" x 7 1/2" with four 1/2" x 3" pieces of dowling inserted into the drilled holes. The 2 pieces of dowling in the back should be glued in flush with the base. The 2 remaining pieces of dowling should be inserted in the 2 front holes, extending 1/2" beyond the base.

CALDECOTT RECORDING FORM

Name _____

Title of Book	Date Completed	Vocabulary	Written Questions	Oral Recall	Art Work	Total Grade